Level 2   Book 2

words

stories

The Gingerbread Man

Stories adapted by Shirley Jackson
Illustrated by Giles Hargreaves
Series designed by Jeannette Slater

Copyright © 1999 Egmont World Limited.
All rights reserved.
Published in Great Britain by Egmont World Limited,
Deanway Technology Centre, Wilmslow Road,
Handforth, Cheshire SK9 3FB
Printed in Germany
ISBN 0 7498 4363 2

old woman

gingerbread man

boy

girl

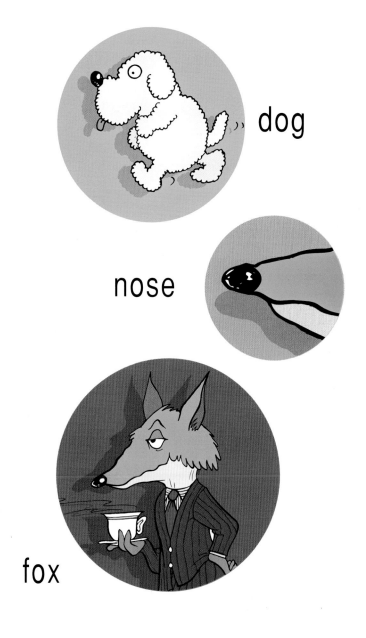

dog

nose

fox

Once upon a time,
an old woman made a
gingerbread man.

new words **an** **made**

The old woman was going to eat the gingerbread man.

new word **going**

But the gingerbread man jumped up and ran away.

new word **up**

"Run, run, as fast
as you can,
You can't catch me,
I'm the gingerbread
man," sang the
gingerbread man.

Run as fast can can't catch I'm sang

A boy saw the gingerbread man.

"Run, run, as fast as you can.

You can't catch me,
I'm the gingerbread
man," sang the
gingerbread man.

A boy and a girl saw
the gingerbread man.

"Run, run, as fast as you can.
You can't catch me,
I'm the gingerbread man," sang the gingerbread man.

o new words

A boy and a girl and
a dog saw the
gingerbread man.

"Run, run, as fast as
you can.

no new words

You can't catch me, I'm the gingerbread man," sang the gingerbread man.

A boy and a girl and a dog and a cat saw the gingerbread man.

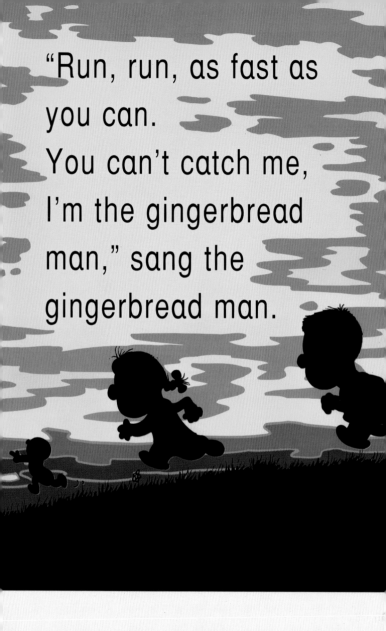

"Run, run, as fast as you can.
You can't catch me, I'm the gingerbread man," sang the gingerbread man.

no new words

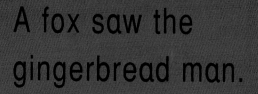

A fox saw the
gingerbread man.

"I will help you," said
the fox. "Jump on my
nose."

new word **Jump nose**

The gingerbread man jumped on the fox's nose. Then...

SNAP!!

ew word   **fox's**

The **fox** can catch the gingerbread man!